PREFACE

THE miscellaneous pieces collected in this volume illustrate Mozart's manner of writing for the clavier at critical moments of his career, beginning with the first tentative essays made at home under his father's eye and ending with the utterance of some of the most intimate thoughts of his mature mind. Included are specimens of practical value to the tyro, the moderately proficient and the well-developed pianist. Most of the examples belong to one or other extreme of Mozart's career. The exceptions are the Minuet in D of 1770; the two short Fugues (neither of them completed by Mozart himself) of about the same date; and the Allegro of an unfinished Sonata (K. 312), which probably belongs to the period of the first group of six sonatas, *i.e.* 1774-1775. The two Rondos, the group of Fantasias and the Suite, the Adagio in B minor and the Jig, works of his later years inspired by ideals other than those of a complacent gallantry and the greatest amusement of the greatest number, belong to Mozart's Bach-Handel period; that is, the period, beginning in 1782, of his researches among the works of those composers, which had the consequence that some of Mozart's own writings at that time are deliberately archaic in their form and manner.

The chronological order of the earliest extant works is as follows:

Minuet in F (K. 2), January, 1762.
Allegro in B flat (K. 3), March 4, 1762.
Minuet in F (K. 4), May 11, 1762.
Minuet in F (K. 5), July 5, 1762.
Minuet and Trio in G (K. 1), about the end of 1762.

Investigation of Mozart's works and their circumstances since Köchel compiled his catalogue has resulted in a re-classification of a certain number of his compositions in accordance with the fuller knowledge gained. Correcting the older supposition, which put the long Minuet and Trio at the head of the list, we now recognize the simple Minuet in F (K. 2) as Mozart's first extant work, and the Allegro in B flat as its next successor. The innate perception of the necessary unity in a work of art which Mozart always strove to accomplish is already apparent in both these experiments of his childhood. In the first it is achieved in the supple use of a single figure; the second, a miniature sonata-form movement, illustrates the application of the ternary design which Leopold Mozart had already copied from Emanuel Bach, and therefore taught to his son. The same design applied to the first two Minuets is afterwards dropped in the third and fourth in favour of the alternative form in which the first idea is absent from the *reprise* in the tonic.

Two later Minuets in D (Nos. 5 and 6)—contrapuntal examples in a complete ternary form—differ from one another as a sketch from a mature and thoughtful work, where similar means are employed to different ends. The imitative style of the simple, vivacious Minuet, No. 5 (hastily sketched, one might suppose), reflects naturally the composer's absorption in contrapuntal studies at Bologna during 1770. But in the Sixth Minuet (written in 1789 or 1790) independent flowing counterpoints woven among closely crowded chromaticisms and richly variegated harmony, sequential progressions in either direction coupled with unexpected dissonance and accelerated movement—such resources used with a mastery of concentration intensify the emotion which stirs within the brooding phrases of a perfectly balanced poem.

FANTASIAS, FUGUES, SUITE.

Fantasia and Fugue in C, March or April, 1782.
Fantasia in C Minor, during 1782-1784.
Fantasia in D minor, during 1782.
Suite in C, during 1782.

Why did Mozart not use these forms for clavier composition in the early stages of his career? Probably, because each of them, in his day, was slightly old-fashioned. The popular show pieces of the time were the Rondo and the Variation. The Fantasia had a long history, going back to the very beginning of the dissociation of instrumental from vocal music. And not only was the Suite giving place to the Sonata, but this itself was undergoing the change from the binary to the ternary form. The interest of keyboard composers was focussed here; and of the making of sonatas there was no end. As Wolfgang's earliest essay in sonata form (Allegro, K. 3) shows us, the Mozart family in Salzburg was already familiar with the experiments of Emanuel Bach in Northern Germany. Later, the mere circumstances and demands of his mode of life restricted Mozart's attention to contemporary events and developments in musical art to which as a practical musician he was contributing. It was not until he took up a permanent residence in Vienna that Mozart began to make deep and extensive acquaintance with the works of Handel and Sebastian Bach. From 1782 onwards a new world was revealed to him in the works of these composers which the Court librarian had collected. Not only were they regularly and exclusively played at Baron Van Swieten's house, but Mozart was allowed to take the copies home. He, too, began to make a collection of the Fugues of Handel and of the three Bachs, Sebastian, Emanuel and Friedmann. The Fantasias (including that attached to the Sonata in Vol. I.), the Fugue in C major, and the three movements of an unfinished Suite are some of the fruits of the stimulus of this study.* Of

---

* The two short Fugues (K. 153 and 154) do not belong to this period, being exercises of boyhood only partly written by Mozart and completed by another hand.

the immediate occasion of the composition of the Fugue in C major with its introductory Prelude Mozart gives his own enthusiastic account when sending them with a letter to his sister on April 20, 1782. Constance Weber, shortly to become his wife, was the cause, he says, of the appearance of the Fugue. She had often heard him improvising Fugues, but, on his admission that he had not yet written any, she became insistent that he should do so. The manuscript is now lost, but in it, according to his own account, the Prelude followed the Fugue because he had composed the Fugue first and while writing it was thinking out the Prelude. Mozart also explains to his sister that he affixed the title *Andante maestoso* to the Fugue as an explicit warning against a rapid tempo. " If a fugue is not played slowly," he writes, " one cannot clearly grasp the subject when it appears, and so its effect is nil." The resemblance of its subject to that of the first of the " 48 " may attract notice, though the upward stepping fourths and downward fifths are a familiar enough type. In the event, the general style turns out to resemble Handel's rather than Bach's. A student whose part-playing has not become very exact may be more happy with this Fugue than with many of the " 48 " on account of elements of modern pianistic style, such as sequences of double notes in parallel motion, which tend to reduce part-playing to its most encouraging and agreeable aspect. This applies also to the *fugato* section of the Overture to the Suite in C, where, apart from the inversion of its subject on three occasions, the Allegro has little else of specifically contrapuntal interest. In the three-voice Fugue attached to the Fantasia, however, we have a more shapely, Bach-like Subject issuing, at the moment of the entry of its Answer, in a flowing countersubject which impinges against the first seven notes of the theme in a series of dissonant appoggiaturas. Augmentation of the subject occurs but once, at bar 28, when the Stretti first appear; Diminution follows at bar 36. Handel's influence specially pervades also the other movements of the Suite which, incidentally, Mozart left incomplete, having broken off after writing only six bars of a Sarabande to follow the Courante. The Overture proceeds in the stately French manner which Handel adopted from Lully. The preponderance of the Handelian influence can easily be seen by playing any familiar French Courante by Bach, such as that in the B flat Partita or in the D minor French Suite with its vivacious, strongly rhythmic dance character, and contrasting it with examples from Handel and with the suave, undulatory style of Mozart's Allegretto from which the impulse of the dance has receded. In all three movements of the Suite signs of Mozart's personal touch will not be missed by the student who knows it, especially in the chromatic passages. Noteworthy, too, is the independence with which, contrary to the ancient custom, Mozart has introduced from the more modern sonata the principle of key contrast for successive movements and has even ended his fugal Allegro on the dominant to lead directly to the Allemande. The Courante was to be followed by a Sarabande in G minor. Conversely, the famous Sonata in A imitates the older Suite by keeping the same key for all movements, as do Beethoven's Op. 2 in F minor, Op. 26 in A flat, Op. 27 in C sharp minor; Op. 78, 90, 109 and 111.

Mozart's Fantasias, of course, reflect what he had observed of the special qualities of the *genre* as it had been developed by Sebastian and Emanuel Bach. Some of these had peculiar affinity with the æsthetic predilections of his own nature. J. S. Bach had applied the title indifferently to movements of such widely divergent significance as the two-part Invention-like introduction to the third Partita and the brilliant rhapsody known as the Chromatic Fantasia. The contribution of vocal art to the instrumental Fantasia naturally included the elements of aria, recitative and the cadenza. The early attempts on keyboard instruments to reproduce elaborate vocal *fioriture* were so hampered by vocal traditions, which naturally tended to prefer conjunct passages, that they resembled so many scrawls of an untutored hand rather than shapely, disciplined curves of melody and ornament. Early Toccatas are crowded with such meanderings; the student, if not familiar with their appearance, can easily find examples in published selections from English Virginal books in pieces under various titles. The device of breaking up vocal homophonic progressions into arpeggi on the keyboard was a discovery of liberal resources which helped to unify for purposes of keyboard composition the separate peculiarities of vocal and digital art. Of the Fantasia, in the developed state that we are accustomed to think of it, a dominant quality is that of a certain restlessness. This is not the result merely, or mainly, of rambling figurations and cascades of arpeggi, but rather corresponds to a sort of psychical experience of expecting the unexpected which is created by the meeting of elements such as bold harmonic novelties, kaleidoscopic transformations of one dissonance immediately into another, rhythmical irregularities and changes of time signature, alterations of pace, dramatic pauses. Such elements were stressed by Emanuel Bach who adopted from his father the ornate type found in the Chromatic Fantasia and in the Organ Fantasia in G minor.

As to Mozart, he has made his own contribution towards provoking surprise at the very outset of his Fantasia in C major by beginning, not as a Bach with the rolling arpeggio (*cf.* Mozart, D minor Fantasia) or flourish of scale passage, but as a Haydn solemnly introducing a Symphony. The omission from this Fantasia of an aria-like episode was presumably calculated so as to detain the mind in suspense and not weaken, by anticipating, the ultimate effect of the entry of the Fugal theme (*cf.* the Chromatic Fantasia). A particularly arresting, and, for that time, novel tonal effect (said to be derived from Emanuel Bach) appears at bars 23-27, and is subsequently repeated, where repeated strokes as of the clanging of bells of contrasted pitch ring out against an accompaniment of moving triplets. It is hardly less a surprise that this device should recur, just when the Fugue seems nearly due, at a climax of torrents of arpeggi. Parallels to details of the keyboard writing are plentiful in the

Chromatic Fantasia. Incidentally it is worth noting that the Prelude in B flat in the first book of the "48" is an excellent simple example of the general spirit of a Fantasia.

In the Fantasia in D minor Mozart makes melody the pivotal feature, reversing the method of Emanuel Bach who treats it more as an episode in the scheme. Here Mozart makes the rhapsodical elements incidental and subsidiary to the recurring melodic idea. But the former of the two melodies included fails to complete the course of an aria and breaks up into detached recitative-like figures of varied rhythmical patterns. The sighing figures of bar 23 foll. recall the phraseology of Beethoven in the similarly reiterated chords in the Adagio of Opus 110.

To this Fantasia the strong contrast of the separate Fantasia in C minor (K. 396) lies not only in its strictness of form, but in the intimate blending of the respective peculiarities of melody and instrumental accompaniment. In this Fantasia also, undoubtedly, the melody's the thing, and is given the freedom of the keyboard to range beyond the limits of any single type of voice, and more in the manner of violin or clarinet. But the instrumental arpeggio and rapid scale passages are so wrought and dovetailed into the melodic texture that, instead of figuring independently as the apparatus of an episode or cadenza, they are mingled everywhere in the general design and become integral factors of a subject intended for development.

VARIATIONS.

Variations on "Unser dummer Pöbel meint," Vienna, August 25, 1784.
Variations on "A Minuet by Mr. Duport," Potsdam, April 29, 1789.
Variations in A (K. 137 App.), Vienna, 1789.

The attractive form of instrumental art, known as the Theme and Variations, represented in more than one early type, underwent considerable changes during the eighteenth century. Long before this, the definite attempt had been made to prolong during an extended movement the vitality inherent in some short tune. Everyone knows, for example, the variations by Byrd on *The Carman's Whistle*, of special interest in connection with the type used by Mozart, since it is one of the earliest examples for keyboard of the melodic variation as distinct from that founded on the harmonic basis. Of the latter a contemporary specimen, hardly less familiar, *Les Buffons*, by John Bull, anticipates in its figurations the Handelian manner.

Apart from the natural human impulse to flee monotony, an immediate stimulus towards a system of variations on a theme as we know them in musical art lay in a practical cause. Court dances were long; the tunes which accompanied them were short. Their repetition became intolerably wearisome, and inevitably led the player to indulge in extempore variation and ornament. In the seventeenth century an *Air à danser* or *Air de cour* had its variant or Double. From the point of view of the dance it was obviously desirable to preserve the original rhythm clearly in the variation, and

some recognizable semblance of the tune. But the vagaries of instrumentalists when left to expose their undisciplined ideas of decoration led to counter measures of self-protection on the part of the various composers even before Emanuel Bach's famous protest against similar abuses in connection with the *Reprises* of the Sonata. By printing their Doubles, composers such as Couperin and Rameau gave permanent testimony to their views about legitimate artistic ornamentation of a melody the lines of which were to be recognizably retained. Of Rameau the best known examples are the two Doubles of *Les Niais de Sologne* and the popular Gavotte in A minor with its six Doubles. (See also Couperin, *Les Canaries.*) In Bach's works the term survives, in the first and second English Suites, in the Courante and Sarabande respectively; and the variations which occur in Handel's harpsichord Suites were, in the first editions, called Doubles, *e.g.* those known as The Harmonious Blacksmith in the Suite in E and those (on a theme already elaborately ornamented) in the Suite in D minor. The addition of one Double to another in this way became equivalent to those sets of an indefinite number of variations on a theme which became so popular a pre-occupation in the art of the eighteenth century. Though, while this type of variation was continuing to expand, the contrapuntal Passacaglia and Chaconne so prevalent in Italy and Germany during the seventeenth century were exhausted by the time Mozart was born, their last important representative composers being Bach and Handel. But here, too, the composer, though looking on his scheme in a different light from that of the composer of Doubles, was nevertheless constructing sets of variations differentiated from the ornamental melodic type by the condition of the persistence of the melody itself unaltered throughout the movement, while complex contrapuntal devices grew over and around it. The student should compare the simple counterpoints of Purcell's attractive Ground in E minor and of the Chaconne in G minor belonging to the Suite in that key with those which achieve such massive grandeur in the complex Passacaglia in C minor for Organ by Bach and the Crucifixus of the Mass.

In contrast again with this *basso ostinato* type, the German Choral, though capable of different sorts of treatment, naturally drew attention to the melody, placing it in the highest voice and making the features of accompaniment a more secondary consideration. In some examples of the Choral Prelude by J. S. Bach the long notes of the original melody are so sensitively ornamented by the common available devices of trill, appoggiatura, and passing-note as to intensify the serious expressiveness of the original, and give it, at any rate, a heightened meaning, sometimes almost the worth of a new melody. Such instances as *Wenn wir in höchsten Nöthen sind; O Mensch, bewein' dein Sünde gross; Schmücke dich, O liebe Seele* become vehicles of emotional appeal by the sensitive adaptation of ordinary means of melodic ornamentation. But though the available means were identical for every composer, the emotional atmosphere in which the

Choral Prelude developed was, of course, far removed (as even the title-page of the Orgel-Büchlein recalls) from the very mundane *milieu* where Mozart learned his methods.

As to the Handelian variation, it has a frequent peculiarity of attending alternately to melody and accompaniment. Some figuration or other which has served to vary the tune is passed over to the left hand or to an inner part, so that while interest in the melody is deflected to the decorative accompaniment there is no sense of halt in the general progress or of decrease in liveliness of mood (see the Suites in D minor and E already mentioned). Features and methods of keyboard virtuosity brought into prominence by Scarlatti and the spread of the Alberti bass habit gave harpsichord composers and players novel resources when interest in counterpoint was on the wane. The substitution all over Europe during the eighteenth century of the harmonic style for the contrapuntal made comparatively simple the art of brilliant and showy improvisation. To extemporize variations on a given tune by means of a set of technical formulæ more or less stereotyped was no formidable task for a genuine musician possessed of executive skill.

The new style in musical art was already widely diffused when Mozart first travelled outside his native Salzburg. He at once met symptoms of the activity of a spirit destined to interfere at times with his early predilections and to cause confusion among his ideals and the modes of setting them out. When he came to London he found Christian Bach already affected by it. The other masters of his early days, including the two Haydns, though indeed not the austere Padre Martini, succumbed, at any rate partially, to its influence. One of its manifestations might not inadequately be described in the formula "Variety for variety's sake."

The gallant style in variations, intended first and foremost for entertainment, suited Mozart in the character of a Clavier virtuoso. He seems hardly to have looked on the *genre* from any other point of view. In construction and detail of style his later variations for the clavier are essentially identical with the earlier. They are primarily a *genre* apt for an executant's display. The more learned devices of the contrapuntist are conspicuously absent, or, at best, only sketchily represented. Instead, every sort of arabesque and ornamental feature is used which could embellish the line of melody without concealing it. But it is seldom that the sense and character of a theme get really altered during the course of the variations; though in a minor variation of a major tune a pathetic note is often touched, and both here and in a *Lento* variation, the composer's deeper sentiments come forward and the virtuoso is temporarily forgotten in the creative activity of the poet.

NOTE.—In a letter to his father dated from Vienna, March 29, 1783, Mozart gives a glowing account of a concert he had given a week earlier (22nd), at which the Emperor was present. After having played one of his own concertos and some other variations, he was called upon to play again, and improvised on the *Aria*, "Unser dummer Pöbel meint," from Gluck's comic opera, *The Pilgrims of Mecca*. The opera was first performed in 1776. Mozart must have known it well. Its Overture suggested to him the *Alla Turca* of the Sonata in A major. The variations were not written till August 1784. How far they resembled or differed from the original improvisations of nearly eighteen months earlier we have no means of knowing. The Variations on a Theme by Duport belong to April 1789. Jean Pierre Duport was an eminent violoncellist, who taught the Emperor Frederick William II. At the time of Mozart's visit to the Emperor at Potsdam in 1789 with Lichnowsky, Duport was director of the King's music. The Variations in A are an arrangement, with a few modifications for pianoforte, of the *Allegretto con variazione*, which form the Finale of the Clarinet Quintet, composed in September 1789.

Adagio in B minor.
(March 19, 1788.)

It would not have been altogether inappropriate if, on account of the character of some of its detail, this very subjective poem had been called a Fantasia like that other Adagio in sonata form, the Fantasia in C minor (K. 396). Its very first chord calls attention [and recalls the opening of the Andante in B flat in the unfinished Sonata in F (K. 533), written two months earlier] to one prominent characteristic of a Fantasia, the restless harmony and closely packed modulation which here concentrate in the thirteen bars of Development (22-34). The third bar brings another sign of the Fantasia, the break-up of the melodic line into recitative-like figures. Features of keyboard style in the Fantasias also appear, such as (1) a share assigned to the left hand in the melodic design; (2) the alternate play of the left hand in remote registers involving its crossing over the right; (3) decorative passages (*e.g.* bars 17-20), and the manner in which a *cantabile* phrase will resolve into an efflorescence of the ornamental type. Note the link chords (bars 15, 21) and the beautiful Coda with its final cadence phrase in the major key.

Andantino in E flat.

Written at some time in 1790, and intended for an album of John Baptist Cramer, the well-known pianist, who at that time was touring the Continent.

Allegro G minor of a Sonata.
(K. 312.)

The unusual omission from the group of the first six sonatas of an example in a minor key might well have been occasioned by the inclusion of the Dürnitz Sonata (No. 6), whose peculiarities amply provided that variety of aspect at which composers aimed for each several collection of their works.

The detail of this Allegro in G minor so closely resembles much of that in the first five sonatas, whose style owed some characteristics to recent examples of

Joseph Haydn, that its composition must be presumed to belong to the same period, towards the end of 1774, when Mozart was preparing his series for use in view of a tour. In conjunction with these observations, the fact that the movement has remained but a fragment of an unfinished sonata has led critics to suggest that we have before us the actual first movement of a sonata in the minor key which Mozart would have completed and included in that series had not his attention been diverted to the novelties of the French style which he encountered at Münich and copied in the Dürnitz Sonata. The series would undoubtedly have gained, from a poetic standpoint, by the presence of a sonata in the key of G minor. That Mozart enshrined in this tonality some of his most poignant utterances we have the testimony of the two Symphonies, the String Quintet and the Allegro in G minor of the early Milanese Quartet in B flat.

In the Allegro of the Sonata (No. 2) in F major will be clearly recognized several parallels with the language and treatment of this movement, since in both cases the same mannerisms of Haydn are imitated. If the second Exposition, at bar 13, of the initial theme, though like Haydn, is without parallel among Mozart's early sonatas, the long passages of triplet figures, the partition of flowing arabesques between the hands, and a new melodic phrase (at bar 64) to end the Exposition are devices common to these two Allegros and familiar in Haydn's usage. The long Development no less reflects Haydn's ideal in reassembling all the main features of the first section. The only fresh idea introduced at this point is the group of modulating chords, at bars 68, 71, as a link to connect the two main divisions. This detail has special interest, since it is in the same key that Mozart employs the same expressive device with greater intensity in the string Quintet and, most strikingly, in the Finale of the Symphony. On the other hand, just as in the B flat Sonata (No. 3) and in the Dürnitz Allegro, the less idealistic mannerisms in the new French taste betray their influence in the Recapitulation monotonously unvaried except for the necessary transposition into the minor key. This affectation was short-lived with Mozart, and disappeared from his work after 1775.

First Movement of a Sonata in B flat.

Written in 1782. Only ninety-one bars of the movement are in Mozart's autograph, *i.e.* to the end of the Development. The movement was completed by the Abbé Stadler, a friend of Mozart and Haydn, and himself a distinguished composer. In completing this sonata movement he has, naturally, merely copied the text of the first part, making only the necessary modulations.

Adagio for Harmonica.

This piece and a Quintet in two movements for an unusual combination, harmonica, flute, oboe, viola, and 'cello, were written in 1791 (just before the *Magic Flute*) for Marianna Kirchgössner, who, losing her sight in early childhood, became an accomplished performer on the glass harmonica, and in Vienna attracted the interest of Mozart.

AUBYN RAYMAR.

EDITOR'S NOTE AS TO SIGNS USED IN THE TEXT

PEDAL

This has been marked where vitally necessary to the effect, in view of the modern piano, or where desirable in general. To skilled performers many additional pedallings may be possible with success, especially in the slower movements. The sign "P" without any following line indicates the depression and holding of pedal until the next sign "P"—*i.e.*, "legato" pedalling. In all other cases the exact duration of the pedal is clearly marked by a dotted line turned up at the end, thus: P.........⋀

PHRASING

Phrase length and construction is indicated by the use of the curved line ⌒, but this does not necessarily mean "legato" as well. Dots or dashes are used to show staccato or staccatissimo, and the sign ⚲ is used for a particularly sympathetic "mezzo-staccato."

Certain important ornamental *sub-phrasings* will be found indicated at times, such as:

This indicates the delicate details of treatment, whilst the rhythmical phrase line is also shown.

A.B. 431.

CONTENTS

SIX MINUETS

1
MINUET IN F

(Köchel No.2)

W. A. MOZART

2
MINUET IN F

(Köchel No. 4)

3
MINUET IN F
(Köchel No.5)

4
MINUET AND TRIO IN G

(Köchel No. 1)

5
MINUET IN D
(Köchel No. 94)

(a) Originally at this pitch but impossible to stretch in the majority of cases.

A.B. 342

6
MINUET IN D

(Köchel No.355)

Sostenuto (♩ = 100–104)

RONDO
in D

(Köchel No. 485)

W. A. MOZART

RONDO
in A minor

(Köchel No. 511)

W. A. MOZART

(a) as at (a) on page 25   (b) as at (a) on page 26   (c) as at (b) on page 26   (d) ♪♪♪♪ etc.

FANTASIA AND FUGUE
in C

(Köchel No. 394)

W. A. MOZART

FUGUE.

Andante maestoso e cantabile. ($\quad = 69$)

FANTASIA
in C minor

(Köchel No. 396)

W. A. MOZART

un poco agitato e pochiss accellerando

Tempo I

FANTASIA
in D minor
(Köchel No. 397)

W. A. MOZART

Allegretto ($\quarternote = 108$)

mp dolce

TWO FUGUES

1
Fugue in E flat

(Köchel No.153)

W. A. MOZART

Andante con moto ($\quad$ = 112)

A. B. 347

2
Fugue in G minor

(Köchel No.154)

W. A. MOZART

SUITE
in C

(Köchel No. 399)

W. A. MOZART

OVERTURE
Grave (♪ = 76)

ALLEMANDE
Andante (♩ = 66)

COURANTE
Allegretto (♩ = 96)

A LITTLE JIG
in G

(Köchel No. 574)

W. A. MOZART

VARIATIONS

on "Unser dummer Pöbel meint"

(Köchel No. 455)

W. A. MOZART

THEME
Allegretto (♩ = 54–56)

VAR. II

VAR.V
Minore (Tempo I) (♩=54)

VAR.VI
Maggiore

VAR. VII

VAR. VIII
Poco animato

VAR.IX
Adagio (♩ = 44)

VAR. X
Allegro (♩=80–84)

A.B.350

92

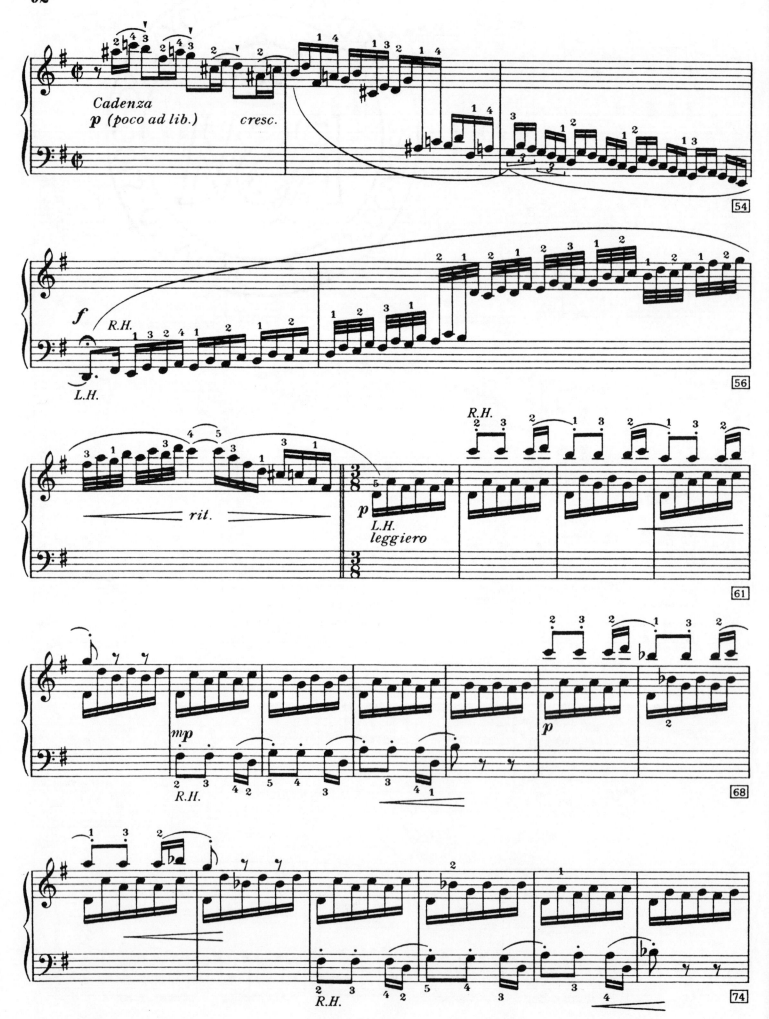

A B 350

Tempo I (Allegretto)

VARIATIONS
on "A Minuet by Mr. Duport"

(Köchel No. 573)

W. A. MOZART

THEME
Allegretto con grazia ($\downarrow$=132)

VAR. III

VAR. V

(a)

VAR.VI
Minore（Poco sostenuto）

VAR.VII
Maggiore（Tempo I ）

VAR. VIII
Adagio (♩ = 84)

VAR.IX
Allegro ($\quarter = 126$)

Coda

VARIATIONS
in A

(Köchel No. 137, of the Appendix)

W. A. MOZART

THEME
Allegretto (♩ = 54)

VAR. I

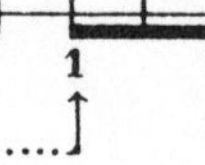

VAR. III
Minore

VAR. IV
Maggiore

VAR. V
Adagio (♩ = 42)

VAR.VI
Allegro (♩= 60)

A. B. 352

ADAGIO
in B minor

(Köchel No.540)

W. A. MOZART

116

A.B.353

ALLEGRO
in B flat

(Köchel No.3)

W. A. MOZART

Allegro moderato ($\bullet$ = 132)

ANDANTINO
in E flat

(Köchel No. 236)

W. A. MOZART

ALLEGRO
of a Sonata

(Köchel No. 312)

W. A. MOZART

FIRST MOVEMENT
of a Sonata
(Köchel No. 400)

W. A. MOZART

(a) As on page 126   *(b)* As on page 126

ADAGIO
for Harmonica*
(Köchel No. 356)

W. A. MOZART

* A graduated set of glass basins or bowls revolving over a trough of water, the moistened glasses being played by application of the fingers